WHAT IS JUNIOR ACHIEVEMENT?

Founded locally in 1953, Junior Achievement of Santa Clara County, Inc. is a nonprofit (501c3) economic education organization which serves area students by providing a series of sequential curriculum enhancement programs spanning kindergarten through senior high school.

In its forty-two year history in Santa Clara County, Junior Achievement has established itself as a leader in business and economics education and workforce readiness programs for young students.

Four programs are available locally: Applied Economics, The Middle Grades Program, Project Math, and The Elementary School Program. Junior Achievement's unique approach places a community volunteer in each classroom.

Junior Achievement is the only program in existence with the sole purpose of enhancing our school curriculum using classroom volunteers, on a continuous basis, with a defined curriculum.

THE BEST OF
TOPICAL FISH / by Podesta

ISBN: 0-9648808-0-6

Library of Congress Catalogue Card Number: 95-090790

THE BEST OF
TOPICAL FISH / by Podesta

Wave Spray Publishers,
Santa Cruz, CA 95062

FOREWARD

Curious little ideas that swim right up to you—that's the joy behind Bob Podesta's Topical Fish. And, we can all learn something from these fish.

Our world changes so rapidly it is comforting to know that simple truths endure. Things your mother taught you (or your teacher tried to). Bits of wisdom passed down through the ages. Ways of making a life that are often lost in the hustle and bustle of making a living. By capturing those powerful ideas in an entertaining form, this book gives us folk remedies for uncertain times.

And they are ideas to be shared.

Handing down these homespun values is central to the work of community. We construct our world from the building blocks we are given. Ideas like those contained in these pages provide a foundation for civil society. They remind us that all people want much the same things: respect, security and the freedom to dream. We have nothing less than an obligation to pass on these universal concepts from one generation to the next.

That's why this limited edition to benefit Junior Achievement is so special. Proceeds from the sale of the book support worthwhile education programs that help our kids succeed in business. The wisdom of these ideas will help them succeed at everything else.

Give kids one of these fish and they will think for the rest of their lives.

TOM HAYES
Author, *You Can Make A Difference in Silicon Valley*

When Scott Smith, editor and publisher of The San Jose Business Journal in 1988, saw some of my fish paintings and panels that tied in fish with quotations from the great minds, he asked if I would put the fish to work in a cartoon in Silicon Valley's business newspaper. This was the start of TOPICAL FISH.

Here are two hundred of them for your entertainment and education. I say, "education," because fish are very important in all of our cultures.

For centuries, fish have been symbolic for abundance, wealth, regeneration, harmony and love. Here, in Topical Fish, they're used as a learning tool, following the Losanoff learning system's light-hearted technique to fix in your subconscious mind the wisdom of the world's greatest brains.

If you look at the message and the fish enough times, you'll find yourself following the quotation's suggestion unconsciously!

Perhaps that's why Silicon Valley administration and management people clip Topical Fish from the newspaper and display it prominently!

ROBERT PODESTA

Imagination grows by exercise
and contrary to common belief,
is more powerful in the mature
than in the young.
W. SOMMERSET MAUGHAM

Do you wish people to
believe great of you?
..don't speak.
PASCAL

Who reflects too much will
accomplish little.
VAN SCHILLER

Whatever advice you give,
be brief.

HORACE

A little pot boils easily.
DUTCH PROVERB.

We should call every
truth false which is not
accompanied by at
least one laugh..
NIETZCHE

Anybody who is any
good is different from
everybody else.
FELIX FRANKFURTER

The essence of pleasure
is spontaneity,
GERMAINE GREER

One can never consent to creep when
one feels the impulse to soar.
                    HELEN KELLER

Just to be active is a
grand thing.
                AGATHA CHRISTIE

To be wronged is nothing
unless you continue to
remember it.
CONFUSCIOUS

The greater the difficulty the
more glory in surmounting it.
EPICURES

You never know what is enough
unless you know what is more
than enough.
WILLIAM BLAKE

Less is more.
BROWNING

Nothing is so good as
it seems beforehand.
GEORGE ELLIOT

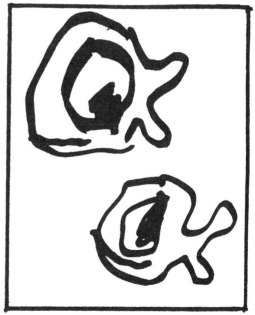

It is not every question
that deserves an answer.
PUBLILIUS SYRUS

It is wonderful how much may
be done if we are always doing.
THOMAS JEFFERSON

For age is opportunity..
no less than youth.
LONGFELLOW

You have to love your children unselfishly.
That's hard, but it's the only way.
BARBARA BUSH

Keep up appearances
whatever you do.
CHARLES DICKENS

**Substitute a better habit for the
one we're trying to change.**
ROBERT WATERMAN, JR.

Aim high. If you aim at nothing, you will hit nothing.
LOGAN P. SMITH

Hitch your wagon to a star.
EMERSON

Nearly all men can stand adversity,
but if you want to test a man's
character, give him power.
ABRAHAM LINCOLN

What we get out of government depends
directly on who we got into government.
CALVIN MACKENZIE

The best things in life are
appreciated most after
they are lost.
ROY L. SMITH

Give people flowers when
they can smell them.
NICOLAS CAUSSIN

The lonely one offers his hand
too quickly to whomever he
encounters.
NIETZCHE

The great end of life is not
knowledge but action.
HUXLEY

There is the greatest practical benefit
in making a few failures early in life.
THOMAS HENRY HURLEY

To win an argument
is to lose a friend.
DANIEL WEBSTER

Don't win the argumenmt
and lose the sale.
ROY L. SMITH

A true leader always keeps
an element of surprise
up his sleeve.

CHARLES de GAULLE

Because a friend is polite do
not think his time is valueless.
SOLON

If you are angry, at least, pause
before you speak.
JOHN LUBBOCK

**Think wrongly if you please,
but in all cases, think for yourself.**
DORIS LESSING

**When you know all the
answers, you haven't
asked all the questions.
HAL STEBBINS**

**Strong reasons make strong actions.
SHAKESPEARE**

Pleasure is the object, the duty, and the goal of all rational creatures.
VOLTAIRE

Fair and softly goes far.
CERVANTES

He who defines his conduct by ethics
imprisons his song bird in a cage.
KAHIL GIBRAN

The quality of life is
determined by its activities.
ARISTOTLE

Great favorites have many
admirers but few friends.
REINHOLD NIEBUHR

If I rest, I rust.

MARTIN LUTHER

**Happiness is brief
it will not stay, God
batters at the sails..
EURIPIDIES**

**My trade and art is
to live.
MONTAGNE**

There is no duty we so much underrate,
as the duty of being happy.
ROBERT LOUIS STEVENSON

He has not learned the first lesson of life who
does not every day surmount a fear.
RALPH WALDO EMERSON

Every day in every way I am getting better and better.
EMILE COUE.

Age is a matter of feeling, not years.
DONALD CURTIS

**If you are kind and sympathetic
your advice will be often sought.**

JOHN LUBBOCK

**No one can be in perfect
accord with any one but himself.
SCHOPENHAUER**

Intuition is given to him who has
undergone long preparation for receiving i
LOUIS PASTEUR

Man never rises to great
truths without enthusiasm.
VAUVENARGUES

**Man is obviously made to think.
It is his whole dignity and his
whole merit.**
PASCAL

Taste is the only morality.. Tell me
what you like and I will tell
you what you are.
RUSKIN

Your children need your
presence more than they
need your presents.
JESSE JACKSON

Happiness can only be felt if
you don't set any condition.
ARTHUR RUBENSTEIN

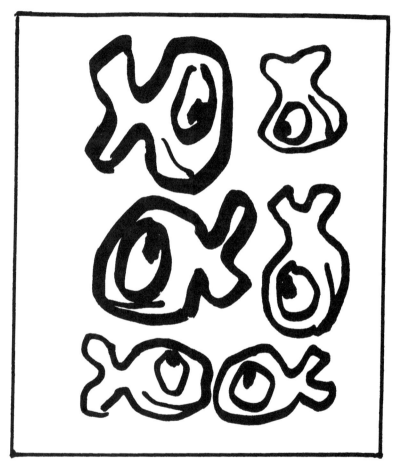

Thinking is like loving and dying.. each of us must do it for himself.
                    JOSIAM ROYCE

The most agreeable thing in
life is worthy accomplishment.
EDGAR HOWE

Caution is the eldest
child of wisdom.
VICTOR HUGO

We are all in the gutter, but
some of us are looking
at the stars.
OSCAR WILDE

The deepest principle in
human nature is the craving
to be appreciated.
WILLIAM JAMES

Yesterday I dared to struggle..
Today I dare to win.
BERNADETTE DEVLIN

You may be disappointed if
you fail, but you are doomed
if you don't try.
BEVERLY SILLS

There is no substitute
for paying attention.
DIANE SAWYER

If you think you can, you can and if you think you can't, you're right.
MARY KAY ASH

**Argument is the worst
sort of conversation.**
JOHNATHAN SWIFT

**To be able to find joy in another's
joy: that is the key to happiness.**
GEORGES BERNANOS

Don't find fault. Find a remedy.
HENRY FORD

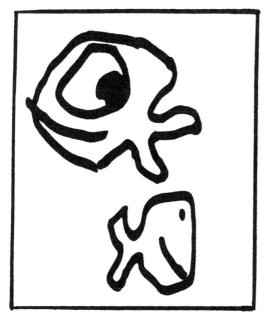

Men have become the tools of their tools.
HENRY DAVID THOREAU

**Better to ask twice than
to lose your way once.**
DANISH PROVERB

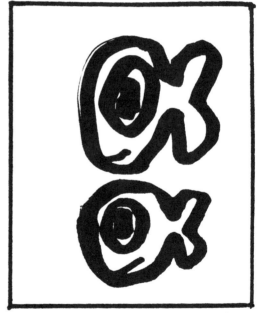

Art is the great stimulus of life.
NIETZSCHE

Better to ask twice than
to lose your way once.
DANISH PROVERB

Art is the great stimulus of life.
NIETZSCHE

The greatest remedy
for anger is delay.
SENECA

Ambition and love are the
wings to great deeds.
GOETHE

A leader is a dealer in hope
NAPOLEON BONAPARTE

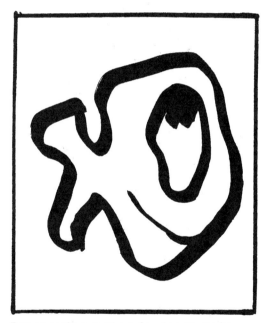

Preparation makes for leadership
DR. DOUGLAS FREEMAN

**When anger rises, think
of the consequences.**
CONFUCIOUS

**If you wish to gain
affection, bestow it.**
SENECA

The man worthwhile is the man who
can smile when everything goes wrong.
ELLA WHEELER COX

I go for two kinds of men: -the kind
with muscles, and the kind without.
MAE WEST

The moments when you have really lived
are the moments when you have done things
in the spirit of love..
HENRY DRUMMOND

In the middle of difficulty
lies opportunity..
ALBERT EINSTEIN

Gold is tried in fire, brave
men by adversity.
SENECA

I like business, because each
day is a fresh adventure.
R. H. CARABELL

Real generosity is doing something nice for someone who'll never find out.
FRANK A. CLARK

Nothing in the world can take the place of persistence.
CALVIN COOLIDGE

There is no education
like adversity.
DISRAELI

As a rule, adversity reveals genius
and prosperity conceals it.
HORACE

With money in your pocket, you
are wise, and you are handsome,
and you sing well too.
           YIDDISH PROVERB

The final test of a gentleman: his
respect for those who can be of no
possible value to him.
WILLIAM LYON PHELPS

It's not the men in my life that
count   -it's the life in my men!
MAE WEST

**Adversity leads the
wise to prosperity.**
GORDON

The sign brings customers.
LA FONTAINE

Ability is a poor man's wealth.
BAUDJUIN

To open a shop is easy: -the
difficult thing is keeping it open.
CHINESE PROVERB

The only difference between a man of
forty and a man of seventy is thirty
years of experience.
MAURICE CHEVALIER

The buck stops with the
guy who signs the checks..
RUPERT MURDOCH

Skillful pilots gain their
reputation from storms
and tempests
       EPICURES

Without adventure, civilization
is in full decay.

A. N. WHITEHEAD

He who has not tasted bitter
does not know what sweet is.

FROM THE GERMAN PROVERB

The foundation stone for
any achievement is desire.
CLEMENT STONE

The reserve of readiness
is the secret of all achievement.
O.S. MARDEN

I look at every day as lost
in which I do not make a
new acquaintance.
SAMUEL JOHNSON

The spur of the moment is the
essence of adventure.
ANTONY ARMSTRONG JONES

The difference between men and boys
is the price of their toys.
LIBERACE

You don't win once-in-a-while.. You
don't do things right, once-in-a-while..
You do them right all of the time.
VINCE LOMBARDI

The definition of a beautiful
woman is one who loves me.
SLOAN WILSON

It is well to think well. It is
devine to act well.

HORACE MANN

Act as though it were impossible to fail.

DOROTHEA BRANDE

To achieve great things, we
must live as though we
were never going to die.

VAUVENARGUES

The harder you work, the
luckier you get.
GARY PLAYER

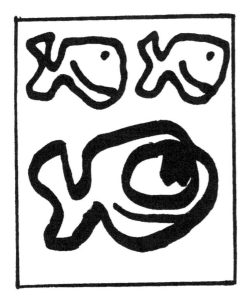

Imagination is more
important than knowledge.
ALBERT EINSTEIN

Be great in act as you have been in thought.
SHAKESPEARE

Life is not measured in hours, but in accomplishments.
PIKE

Act the part and you will play the part.

WILLIAM JAMES

The life of achievement is a life of hard work.

COUNCILLOR

I cannot do everything, but still, I can do something; I will not refuse to do the something I can do..
HELEN KELLER

Always be a little kinder than necessary..
JAMES M. BARRIE

The greatest thing in the
world is to know how to be
one's own.
        MONTAGNE

If you obey all the rules
you miss all the fun.
KATHERINE HEPBURN

We need the faith
to go a path untrod.
EDWIN MARKHAM

Who never walks save where he sees
man's tracks, makes no discoveries.
J. G. HOLLAND

A ship in harbor is safe, but that
is not what ships are built for.
JOHN SHEDD

The more is given, the less people will
work for themselves, and the less they
work, the more their poverty will increase.
TOLSTOI

How old would you be
if you didn't know how
old you was?
SATCHEL PAIGE

Our happiness depends
on wisdom all the way..
SOPHOCLES

If I listen, I have the advantage.
If I speak, others have it.

FROM THE ARABIC

It is always the adventurers who
accomplish great things.

MONTESQUIEU

The art of life lies in a constant readjustment to our surroundings.
OKARURA KAKUZO

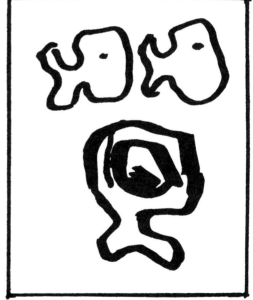

Thy actions, and thy actions alone, determine thy worth.
LICHTE

Happiness is in the taste and not in the things..
LA ROCHEFOUCALD

Too low they build who build beneath the stars ,
EDWARD YOUNG

**Think wrongly if you please,
but in all cases, think
for yourself..**
DORIS LESSING

People who know how to
act are never preachers.
EMERSON

Do not be too moral.. you may
cheat yourself out of much life.
HENRY DAVID THOREAU

Every day should be distinguished by at least one particular act of love.
LAVATER

Thought is the seed of action.
EMERSON

The happy man is not
he who seems thus to
others but who seems
thus to himself..

PUBLILIUS SYRUS

Not failure but low aim is crime.
JAMES RUSSELL LOWELL

**Imagination grows by exercise
and contrary to common belief
is more powerful in the mature
than in the young.**
          W. SOMMERSET MAUGHAM

**Application in youth
enriches old age.
CHARLES SIMMONS**

**A good appearance is
a premium everywhere.
LA FONTAINE**

To accept good advice is but
to increase one's own ability.
GOETHE

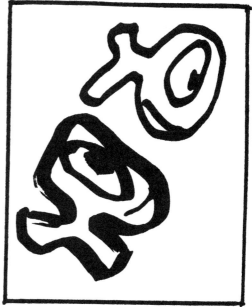

Many receive advise, only
the wise profit by it.
PUBLILIUS SYRUS

One of the marks of real success
in life is to believe that there's
a reason for everything.
KEN BLANCHARD

"Don't talk about it, do it!"
CHARLOTTE BEERS

To accept good advice is but
to increase one's own ability.
GOETHE

There is no obstacle that there is
some way around, or over, or through.
ROBERT COLLIER

Who seems most
kingly is king.
THOMAS HARDY

I'd like to thank God, because She makes everything possible.
HELEN REDDY
(Accepting her Grammy Award)

Man is not made for defeat...
ERNEST HEMINGWAY

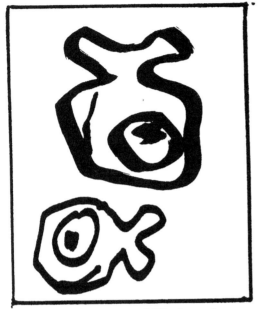

The great enemy of life is not knowledge, but action.
ALDOUS HUXLEY

Action makes more fortunes than caution.
VAUVENARGUES

Cultivate our faculties;
you must either use them
or lose them.
JOHN LUBBOCK

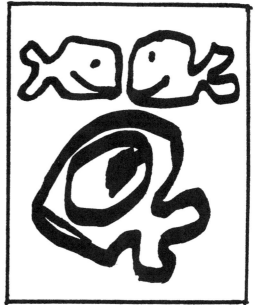

Character is just as important
as ability.
DON SHULA

Talk happiness. The world is sad enough
without your woe. No path is wholly rough.
WILCOX

When one has not had a good father,
one must create one.
NIETZSCHE

All that we need to make us really happy
is something to be enthusiastic about.
KINGSLEY

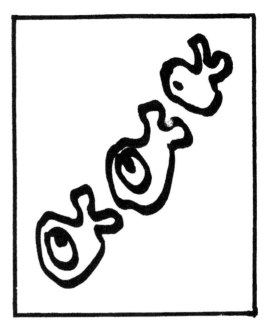

It is in the enjoyment and not in mere possession that makes for happiness.
MONTAGNE

The only true happiness comes from squandering ourselves for a purpose.
WILLIAM COWPER

Of all nature's gifts to the human race,
what is sweeter to man than his children.
CICERO

Action is the antidote to despair.
JOAN BAEZ

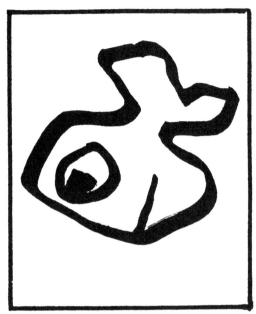

To be successful, the first thing to do
is to fall in love with your work.
SISTER MARY LAURETTA

Write it on your heart that
every day is the best day in the year.
EMERSON

**Children require guidance and sympathy
far more than instruction.**
ANNE SULLIVAN

You have to love your children unselfishly.
That's hard, but it's the only way.
BARBARA BUSH

If you want the rainbow,
you gotta put up with the rain.
DOLLY PARTON

The beginning is giving.
MURIEL RUKEYSER

You have to be true to yourself
before you can give your best to others.
NANCY WILSON

If you can give your son only
one gift, let it be enthusiasm.
BRUCE BARTON

Our greatest glory is not in never falling,
but in rising every time we fall.
CONFUCIUS

The great, successful people of the world
think ahead and create their mental picture,
and then go to work materializing their mental
picture. ROBERT COLLIER

ABOUT THE CARTOONIST

Robert Podesta creates three different cartoons—each illustrating quotations, proverbs and sayings.

This cartoon, Topical Fish, appears in business newspapers in different parts of the country.

His fish also are featured to illustrate Hawaiian proverbs in the morning newspaper in Honolulu, The Honolulu Advertiser.

Texans have seen his dogs illustrating quotations in his cartoon, Guide Dogs for the Mind.

His studio, located on a cliff, overlooking the Monterey Bay in Santa Cruz, California, is a library of quotation and proverb books of all languages. From this source he creates a series of messages that he hopes will amuse and help the reader enjoy a happier life.

He attributes his wonderful life to the help received from good guidance from many sources. He wants to pass this on.

His guidance cartoons present a convenient and pleasant way of reminding us to take action on the good advice.